RaisingBaby:

A Pocket Guide to

Baby's 1st Year

Nina Vaid Raoji

RN, MSN, APN-CPNP

RaisingBaby: A Pocket Guide to Baby's 1st Year

Published by RaisingBaby, LLC

ISBN: 978-0-9859021-0-0

Printed in the United States of America

The information included in this guide is for educational purposes only. It is not intended nor implied to be a substitute for professional medical advice. The reader should always consult his or her child's healthcare provider to determine the appropriateness of the information for their own situation.

Baby _____ Firsts:

Smiled

_____

Rolled over

_____

1st Tooth

_____

Held bottle

_____

Ate solids

_____

Crawled

_____

1st Word

_____

Slept thru night

_____

Walked

_____

BIRTH:

Height_____ Weight _____

1 mo: Height_____ Weight_____

2 mos: Height_____ Weight_____

3 mos: Height_____ Weight_____

4 mos: Height_____ Weight_____

5 mos: Height_____ Weight_____

6 mos: Height_____ Weight_____

7 mos: Height_____ Weight_____

8 mos: Height_____ Weight_____

9 mos: Height_____ Weight_____

10 mos: Height_____ Weight_____

11 mos: Height_____ Weight_____

1 YEAR:

Height_____ Weight _____

Foreword

there! If you bought this pocket guide, you now have an incredibly **SIMPLE** tool to help you get through baby's first year. My name is Nina Raoji and by profession I am a pediatric nurse practitioner. I started my nursing career working as a pediatric ICU nurse and then went back to school to get my Masters in Pediatric Nursing from the University of Pennsylvania, School of Nursing. I then worked in a pediatric emergency department, followed by a job in a children's developmental and behavioral clinic. I have worked with very sick kids, happy, healthy kids and everything in between.

Over the span of two years starting in 2010, I have been blessed with the birth of my daughter, Naya, and five wild nephews. Alongside my family, I have an amazing group of 12 friends, all with kids born within six months of my baby girl. With all this combined professional and real life experience, I decided to compile a set of guidelines for that first year, using concepts that worked for most of us (although they were definitely tweaked here and there by each of us).

As first time parents, my husband and I had wished many times that we had a simple set of guidelines to help us get started in taking care of our daughter. Whether it was sleep schedules or feeding schedules, we just wanted a jumping off point. We figured we were not alone in feeling this way. Even though there are lots of parenting books out there, we felt none were very concise or easy-to-use. There are SO many things going on during baby's first year that it is almost too much to take in, let alone remember – at least until it's over. So, I decided to write this short guide to help you (mommy, daddy, grandma, grandpa, etc.) organize your mind, your goals, and you sanity! It's also a GREAT way to get everyone on the same page.

I want to emphasize one very important matter: **NO TWO CHILDRE ARE THE SAME**. This guide is written simply as a starting point! If you child is doing something earlier or later than stated in this guide, d not panic. Your pediatric provider will alert you of any concerns. S relax and enjoy the ride (or at least try)!

The contents in this book have been set up to give you information fc the span of two months at a time. I suggest reading the next chapter couple of weeks in advance to get a heads up of what is to come. I each chapter, *developmental milestones* are intended to be achieve by the <u>end</u> of those two months and *goals to work towards* are for th following two months. Please take these guidelines as *tools* to hel you, rather than 'set in stone' rules. Babies do things at their ow pace, as they are ready, so don't force them! Your baby will tell yo when he or she is ready to make the next move... Now, let's ge started!

Table of Contents

BEFORE BABY ARRIVES:

- **Visit baby websites** and sign up for information, coupons, emails, offers, samples, etc. Some example websites include:
    - Similac.com
    - Enfamil.com
    - Gerber.com
    - BabyCenter.com
    - Amazon.com/mom
    - AAP.org (the American Academy of Pediatrics, AAP)
    - Healthychildren.org (a consumer-directed AAP website)
    - Kidshealth.org (from Nemours, a non-profit organization)

- **CORD BLOOD/TISSUE BANKING** – Think about whether you want to save cord blood and / or tissue and with which company (e.g. CBR, Viacord). Ask about any discounts they offer (e.g. nursing discount). They will send you a kit to take with you for when baby is delivered, so DON'T FORGET to put the kit in your hospital bag

- **Choose a pediatrician.** Have his or her name, address and phone number with you when you go to the hospital.
    - *** You may want to schedule an interview with the pediatrician before baby is born to ask about the practice, provider coverage for when the practice is closed (weekends) and to see if your personalities "mesh."

- **Don't go overboard.** All you need for baby's crib is a crib sheet, and, if you must, a Breathable Bumper. Don't waste money on expensive bedding, blankets, toys, etc. Basics like crib sheet, bibs, burp cloths, sleep & play one piece snap ups, diapers and wipes should suffice in the first month!

- **Take a CPR class.** There should be free classes offered in your community. Try to get family to take the class with you!

BABY'S 1ST YEAR OVERALL:

A few random thoughts to remember as you journey through baby's 1st year:

Cherish every single moment - they grow up so fast!!!

Read, read, read to baby – from day one (or once you get settled at home). Reading helps build first sounds, first words, vocabulary, conversation and so much more.

Keep baby facing you when in the stroller – this helps reduce anxiety and increases parent / child interaction, which is critical for socialization, vocabulary development, and baby's overall happiness. ☺

The car seat should be rear-facing until baby is two years old as per the AAP's latest recommendations.

In cold weather, place a blanket on top of the car seat's safety harness instead of putting multiple layers on baby. Layers create more distance between baby and the seatbelt, decreasing its safety and effectiveness. Feel free to use a hat, gloves and a seat canopy or BundleMe.

Remember: Baby is adjusting to the new world just like you are adjusting to a new life of responsibility; so take things in stride. No matter how frustrated you get, remember that baby is also trying to figure things out. Look into that little face and remember all the things you LOVE about your little munchkin!

Try to get outside as much as possible – great for you and baby!

- If you are alone most of the time, use the **auto-timer** on your camera to capture special moments.

- **ACCEPT HELP** – no one ever got an award for doing it all on his/her own!!!

- Think of (or Google) a cute idea to document growth each month! It will make an adorable frame or album down the road!

- As technology takes over our lives (including cell phones, television, movies, iPad, iPhone, iPod, YouTube videos, computer apps, portable DVD players, gaming consoles, etc), just remember it is not good for baby's development. This 'screen time' decreases the amount of time spent *talking* and *interacting* with baby, which can potentially lead to delays in language development and socialization. So, as per the AAP's recommendations, avoid any of this 'screen time' until baby is at least 2 years old.

ILLNESS

Any fever equal to or above 100.4°F in baby when <u>younger than 2 months old</u> is considered a medical emergency – contact healthcare provider immediately.

- ○ *The most accurate way to take a temperature is rectally. Under the arm is okay too, but you should add $1°F$ to the reading.*

For a **FEVER** when baby is <u>older than 2 months</u> – consult your child's healthcare provider for management, medication and dose.

Unfortunately, **NO medication is recommended to treat cough/congestion for kids <u>under 2 years of age</u>.**
Instead, ease baby's symptoms in these ways:

- ○ Treat baby with steam for 10-15 minutes
    METHOD: Fill the bathroom with steam by turning the shower on hot and closing the door. Be sure to keep baby away from the water. You may hold baby or place in bouncer if baby is more comfortable.
- ○ Use 2-3 saline drops in each nostril and suction mucous before baby feeds.
- ○ Rub a little Baby Vicks on baby's chest and feet and put socks on before sleep.
- ○ Use humidifiers / vaporizers in baby's room. Have them at a close but safe distance from the crib. Cool mist is recommended over warm mist.

GENERAL TID BITS

○ Once baby is rolling, move the crib mattress to middle level.

○ Once baby is sitting or pulling to stand, move the crib mattress to lowest level.

○ Do not place any toys in baby's crib. You want baby to associate the crib with only sleep, not playtime. Do not use the crib for time-outs either.

○ When diapers leave marks on baby's thighs, it's time to move up diaper size. You should be able to easily fit a finger between baby's skin and diaper.

○ Sterilize baby's bottles and feeding parts until 2 months of age, then as desired.

○ Use baby friendly detergent that is free of dyes, scents, perfumes additives for at least for first 6 months (e.g. Dreft, Tide Free, Seventh Generation, etc).

○ Use a barrier ointment with EVERY diaper change, it will protect skin from diaper rash.

JUST when you feel like you've got it down (schedules, habits feeding, what their cries mean, etc), things will change and you will have to adjust.
Just take things *one day at a time*.

!!!! <u>CAUTION</u> !!!!

<u>AVOID HONEY</u> – it contains spores that can cause infant botulism (a potentially life-threatening disease).

WALKERS ARE NO LONGER RECOMMENDED! **Use an Exersaucer or activity center instead, but limit use to 15-20 minutes a day.** Overuse interferes with hip alignment and the natural development of crawling and walking.

NEVER HEAT BREASTMILK OR INFANT FORMULA IN THE MICROWAVE! Microwaving liquids can cause 'hot spots' that can cause burns in baby's mouth and may change chemical properties of breastmilk or formula.

NO JUICE in first year – baby needs "good" calories in order to grow! Juice is usually full of sugar, unless you make it at home.

KEEP HOT LIQUIDS OUT OF BABY'S REACH!!! **(coffee, tea, faucets, pots, kettles, soup, etc) –** It takes one second for baby to reach out and grab something. Hot liquids can cause SEVERE burns to arms, legs, face, or body (coffee tables are not a safe place).

- o If baby gets a minor burn (1st degree = no blisters, no peeling skin), run cool but not ice cold water over area. You may also apply a cool compress and aloe gel. Do not apply any other "remedies" before consulting your child's healthcare provider.
- o If burn is more severe, or you are not sure, have baby evaluated by a healthcare provider. Call provider first, and if recommended / severe, call 911 or go to the ER.

CRYING

Go through checklist:
- Dirty diaper?
- Hungry?
- Tired?
- Needs to burp?
- Wants attention?
- Over-stimulated?
- Uncomfortable (too hot / too cold / clothes)?
- Pain?
- Sick?

Ways to help:
- Address obvious problems - diaper, burp, hunger, clothes.
- **Swaddle** and put baby down for nap / quiet time.
- Sometimes baby gets tired of being held, so let baby "be" in a safe place (bassinet / crib / Pack n' Play).
- Sometimes baby misses you, so hold, sing, read, talk, rock, or play with baby.
- Soothe with **white noise**.

    METHOD: Take baby into bathroom and turn on the fan, hairdryer, or use a vacuum (obviously in safe distances from baby). You can download a white noise phone app too.
- To relieve **BABY GAS**, try bicycling baby's legs.

    METHOD: Place baby on a firm surface and alternate gently pressing bent legs into tummy. Every few cycles, try both legs together. Repeat a few times, and then give baby a break.

Months 0 & 1 – It's ALL about the baby!

SLEEP:

~15-16 hours a day with short periods of awake time.
Always put baby on his/her **BACK TO SLEEP**. Doing so
reduces risk of Sudden Infant Death Syndrome (SIDS).
NOTHING SHOULD BE IN SLEEP AREA EXCEPT BABY!!! No
toys, blankets, teddy bears, decorative items, NOT A THING!
Avoid even hanging burp cloths/ blankets on the crib rail.
Crib bumpers are *no longer recommended* – but if you still
want to use them, use Breathable Bumpers.
Swaddling is encouraged to minimize baby's startle reflex.
White noise helps baby soothe by recreating the sounds of
the womb and drowning out external noise. You can use it
for daytime naps, nighttime sleep and anytime baby is
fussy.
Pacifier use is okay – baby has a need to suck; it is a
newborn reflex.
Nightlights are okay - Stick with red/orange/yellow/white
hues (not blue/green) to reduce interference with baby's
sleep hormones.
Start to establish day and night – Naps should occur in lit
rooms. Sleep at night should be in quiet, dark rooms.
Best bedtime is 7-8 p.m. From day one at home, start
putting baby in the sleep area for the night in this time
frame, maintain dim/dark lights until morning, and maintain
low noise levels throughout the night.

o Try to **maintain the noise level** you are used to during daytime naps so that baby gets accustomed to noise. If you always have a quiet area for sleep, baby will get used to tha and always need it.

NUTRITION:

o **SIGNS OF HUNGER**: lip smacking, rooting, tongue movement, eye fluttering, and hands in mouth.
   *** Crying is a late sign of hunger. ☹

o **For the first 3 weeks, feed on demand;** wake baby every 2-3 hours during day and every 4 hours at night, as baby may be too sleepy to realize he or she is hungry.

o **Breast feed every 2-3 hours** – wear a **scrunchie** on your wrist to help you remember what side to start on. Feed 10-15 minutes each side.

o **Use a breast pump to express breast milk.** Have your partner or family member help with feedings – pump for 1-2 minutes past the last drop to keep supply up, as the pump is not as strong as baby's suck.

o **Bottle feed 2-3oz formula every 2-3 hours**; do not force baby to finish.

o **Trial formula for at least 2-3 weeks** before changing it. If there is an allergic response (rash, diarrhea, excessive gassiness), stop use and consult healthcare provider.

o **Spitting up** is okay in small amounts, even with every feed. If spit up is excessive, consult child's healthcare provider.

Ways to minimize spitting up: burp halfway between feeds. Lay baby at a 15-30 degree angle (car seat usually works) for 15-30 min after feed. ALWAYS try to feed baby in an inclined position, as feeding in a 'flat-on-back' position can lead to ear infections.

Wet diapers ~5-6 /day, **Dirty diapers** ~2-3 /day – but baby may poop with every feed or once every few days. Variations are totally normal as long as the poop is soft. All babies will strain when pooping because they have to poop lying down!

ROWTH:

Height: + 1-1.5 inches in first month

Weight: + 5-7 ounces per week (baby will lose up to 10% of weight in first 10 days and then start gaining again)

Growth spurts are typical around **7-10 days, 2-3 weeks, 1d 4-6 weeks and can last 2-7 days**. Baby will want to nurse ore frequently (up to every hour) during these spurts and may e more irritable. Baby *should* resume old schedule after owth spurt without needing to be re-trained.

EVELOPMENT:

Encourage tummy time on a flat, firm surface **for 1-2 minutes, 2-3 times a day** and increase time as tolerated – this prevents a flat head and increases neck / shoulder strength.

17

- **Baby sees your face** – newborns can see 8-12 inches away.
- Baby enjoys **high contrast and bold shapes** – show baby black, white and red objects (e.g. bulls eye, black dots / squares on paper). Baby prefers your face most of all.
- Baby likes **high-pitched sounds** – talk and sing often to baby.
- Baby will **turn head side to side** while on tummy.
- **Head/neck control** is very weak – so support head at all times.
- **Sneezing** is okay – it's an early reflex that helps clear nasal passages. Baby should not have a cough.
- **Hiccups** early on are okay – it's a sign of an immature nervous system.
- **Equal movements** of both hands, but hands will remain in fists early on.
- At 6 weeks, baby develops a **social smile**. ☺

HEALTH MAINTAINANCE:

- **HANDWASH, HANDWASH, HANDWASH! Parents, grandparents, siblings, visitors, EVERYONE.** It is better to avoid infections than to be too afraid/shy/embarrassed to ask people to wash their hands! (Keep hand sanitizer bottle all over the house as reminders.)
- **FOR GIRLS** - always wipe diaper area **FRONT TO BACK.** **METHOD**: Wipe from pee area to poop area – getting poop in the pee area may cause a urinary tract infection (UTI).
- **FOR BOYS**: make sure the penis is facing <u>down</u> in the diape

1

otherwise pee will leak upwards out of diaper.

Use a **fine/very fine grit nail file** (the pink one) to file baby's nails in first few months – his/her nails are soft, but very sharp! File nails when baby is sleeping.

Continue **circumcision care** if applicable.

Sponge bathe twice a week until cord falls off. Keep area around cord clean and dry. Cleaning around cord with alcohol is no longer required, but still recommended if area gets wet or dirty with poop.

> **METHOD**: Cover baby with towel and place on a safe surface with wash basin and cloths nearby. Wipe from clean to dirty (face, neck, tummy, arms, back, legs, diaper area, hair last). Expose only what you are wiping. Change washcloths as needed.

Only **2-3 baths** needed per week after cord falls off – too much bathing risks drying out newborn skin. **Use moisturizer immediately after bath.**

> **METHOD:** Use a baby safe tub with sling, keep body covered with warm washcloth, wet hair last.

CLEAN with warm washcloth every day/night – under the neck (every feed if there's frequent spit up), armpits, behind ears, and all arm and leg and diaper area creases.

DO NOT use Q-tips for baby's ears – this will push wax in and eventually clog the ear canal. It may also damage ear drum. Instead, use the corner of a wet washcloth or towel. Wax will naturally clear itself out.

With diaper changes - <u>lather</u> **diaper rash ointment (e.g.**

A&D, Desitin, Vaseline) on baby's diaper area to protect it from diaper rash. Only use wipes / washcloths for poopy diaper changes. For pee-only diapers, just change the diape and apply more ointment if needed – this helps avoid dry skin.

o   Give baby **diaper-free time** every day (10-20 minutes):
>   METHOD: Use a tablecloth with a towel and swaddle blanket on top, remove everything and let baby be. ☺ Make sure both the room and your hands are warm or else you *will* get peed on.

PEDIATRIC VISITS:

o   **Well child visit 2-4 days** after bringing baby home or at **1 week** – for weight check and to assess how things are going

o   Weight check visit at **2 weeks**, if weight gain is a concern.

o   **Well child visit** at **4 weeks** – 2nd Hep B vaccine if 1st was administered in hospital (or may get 2nd Hep B shot at 2 month visit)
>   NOTE: You have to request FIRST Hep B vaccine before discharge from hospital.

TID BITS:

o   **ROUTINE ROUTINE ROUTINE:** Babies thrive on a routine because it helps them know what to expect.
So AS MUCH AS POSSIBLE, try to establish a routine that works for you and baby.

o   **DRESSING BABY:** dress baby in one more layer than you would wear.

For winter babies – invest in a **COOL MIST** humidifier (e.g. Crane, Vicks). This helps keep baby's nasal passages moist. Expose baby to 5-10 minutes of window **sunlight** each day for vitamin D synthesis.

You cannot **spoil** baby YET – so cuddle, hug, rock, kiss, love, sing to, and enjoy baby all you want!

READ to baby – you can never start too young. If you pick 1-2 books that are easy reads, you can memorize them and recite them during car rides or when baby is fussy (e.g. Sandra Boynton's *One, Two, Three*).

<u>**SUPERVISE**</u> **ANY time with pets**!!

COLIC – usually starts around 6 weeks. It is defined as crying periods that last 3 hours a day, for 3 or more days a week, for 3 or more consecutive weeks, without a diagnosed cause. Some ways to deal with colic include **swaddling** to create comfort, using **white noise** to re-create sounds of the womb and exposing baby to **vibrations** such as a moving car or bouncer. There is hope; colic *should* pass by ~3 months.

At first you may want to make **bath time** earlier in the day until you are more comfortable with it, then you can make it part of the nighttime routine if you choose to.

Sterilize baby bottles at least for the first 2 months, then as desired.

REPORT <u>**ANY**</u> **FEVER ABOVE 100.4˚F to healthcare provider.**

GOALS TO WORK TOWARDS:

Start to develop a **nighttime routine** (e.g. massage, change, story, milk, kiss, sleep).

- Start to develop a **general routine** – baby thrives on routines and they help you and baby know what to expect.
- Think about **transitioning** from **bassinet to crib** – once baby is rolling, crib becomes necessary.
- Think about **transitioning** baby into a **separate room,** if possible.
- If you are **going back to work soon** – start introducing a bottle so that it is not a new concept when you are gone. Usually sometime in the afternoon is a good time to start, then increase the number of feeds given by bottle.
- **MILESTONE: ROLLING**

  METHOD: Put interesting things on the side of baby to encourage baby to turn. Help baby roll by turning him or her by legs. Once baby starts to understand the movement, rolling won't be too far away.

NOTES:

_____

_____

_____

_____

_____

_____

_____

Months 2 & 3 - Things are looking better!

SLEEP:

~15 hours a day with 2-3 naps/day – stretch of sleep at night will start to get longer (5-6 hours).

Always put baby on his/her **BACK TO SLEEP** – risk of SIDS peaks at 1-3 months.

Put baby down for nap **awake but drowsy** to allow baby to learn to **self-soothe** (a very important skill when baby wakes up in middle of the night).

White noise, swaddling and pacifiers are still OKAY.

Start using a **transitional object** that is only associated with sleep (usually a small blankie or Manhattan Toy's My Snuggly Blankie). At first, ONLY use during naps when baby is monitored.

Continue to **maintain the noise level** you are used to during baby naps. Baby will be more in tune with noise and may wake up with loud sounds, so continue white noise.

ROUTINE, ROUTINE, ROUTINE.

NUTRITION:

Breast milk / formula should still be the ONLY form of nutrition, unless otherwise advised by child's healthcare provider.

Breastfeed every 3-4 hours – if you feel baby is still hungry after breastfeeding, breastfeed for longer or at more frequent intervals to increase supply OR supplement with formula AFTER each breastfeeding session.

- o **Bottle feed 3-5oz formula every 3-4 hours**; do not force baby to finish.
- o Start to **clean baby's gums and tongue** with a small washcloth first thing in the morning and after nighttime bottle (you do not need to do this in the middle of the night). This will help baby prepare for teeth brushing and cleaning.

GROWTH:

- o **Height**: + 1 inch per month
- o **Weight**: + 5-7 ounces per week

 Growth spurt is typical around **3 months**.

DEVELOPMENT:

- o Encourage **tummy time** for **5-10 mins, 3-5 times a day.** Increase time as tolerated.
- o Once baby has good neck control, start using **Bumbo** chair for short periods (3-5 mins) to help baby learn to sit up and support head.
- o **Baby can see 8-15 inches away** and can track objects moving side-to-side. Use interesting toys to help baby practice.
- o Baby is **starting to explore** the surrounding world. Use mirrors, sit baby up supported by pillows and start introducing different textures.
- o When hands are placed at bottom of feet, baby may **push**

down on legs during tummy time – mimicking a frog.

Baby **starts saying "Oohs" and "Aahs**." Talk back to baby taking turns, as this teaches the fundamentals of a conversation.

Baby will **lift head and chest off ground** when on tummy (this will get better as baby's arms get stronger).

Baby can **recognize parents**. YAY! ☺

EALTH MAINTAINANCE:

Continue only **2-3 baths** per week and moisturize after.

Continue **diaper-free time** every day (10-20 minutes).

Continue to **clean with warm washcloth** every day: under the neck (after every feed if there's frequent spit up), in armpits and all arm and leg creases, behind ears.

REPORT ANY FEVER >100.4°F to your healthcare provider until 2 months of age; then REPORT ANY FEVER >102°F (or the temperature parameters specified as reportable by your child's healthcare provider).

EDIATRIC VISITS:

Well child visit at 2 months – VACCINE time. SHOTS: Hep B #2, DTap, Hib, PCV, IPV. By mouth: Rotavirus (see Appendix A for explanations).

Ask child's healthcare provider about **VITAMINS**.

D BITS:

ROUTINE ROUTINE ROUTINE – try to plan outings with baby's routine in mind (e.g. Go out when baby is supposed to be awake and try not to mess with sleep too much. As baby gets better with routine, you can run errands while baby sleeps.).

o   Baby is **starting to make associations**, so think about your habits (constantly holding baby, rocking baby to sleep, etc) and start decreasing / eliminating any "bad" ones.

o   **Transition baby to crib** if not already done and move into a separate room. If neither has yet happened, you may want to do both at once while baby is still in a swaddle.

> *** You may want to sleep with the baby's crib sheet in your bed beforehand so that crib smells of you and comforts baby during transition.

o   Continue to **READ** to baby! At this point you can read any random magazine – it doesn't matter. Baby will like looking at the colors and faces and listening to the sound of your voice.

GOALS TO WORK TOWARDS:

o   **ENFORCE a nighttime routine** (e.g. massage, change, story, milk, kiss, sleep).

o   Create a **larger play area** so baby can start to practice turning side to side and rolling over.

o   **Baby-proof home**: start with immediate areas around baby's play space.

o   Purchase a **sleep sack** for when baby starts to roll over. At this point you will want to wean baby from the swaddle.

o   If you are **going back to work soon** – start introducing a bottle so that it is not a new concept when you are gone.

If baby is bottle feeding and is working hard to get the milk out, think about **going up a nipple size.**

MILESTONE: SITTING

METHOD: Use the Bumbo or surround baby with a Boppy or small pillows to break falls. Place an interesting object in front of baby to encourage him or her to reach forward. This will help baby stay in the sitting position a little longer. As the tummy and back muscles strengthen, baby will get better at sitting!

Months 2 & 3

NOTES:

_____

_____

_____

_____

_____

_____

_____

_____

_____

_____

_____

_____

_____

SLEEP:

~15 hours a day with 2-3 naps/day –stretch of sleep at night will start to get longer (6-8 hours). Put baby on his/her back to sleep; it is okay if baby rolls over on his or her own. As baby starts to learn to **roll over** – you may want to **wean the swaddle.**

> **METHOD**: Week one: take one arm out and keep one arm swaddled. Week two: take the other arm out and swaddle the lower body under armpits. Week three: change to a sleep sack. If baby resists, go back ONE step and try one more week.

White noise still okay.

Use transitional object associated with sleep.

May want to start putting baby **in dim area for naps** now that day / night are established. Start putting baby in crib for all naps and sleep when at home to associate the crib with sleep.

Night waking is common (4-6 times a night), so it is important for baby to learn to self-soothe back to sleep.

> **METHOD**: Let baby cry for 2-3 minutes to see if he/she is able to put self back to sleep. If not, go into the room, gently pat baby for one minute or until baby calms down and then leave room and repeat. DO NOT PICK BABY UP or baby will learn that crying means getting picked up. There are

other sleep training methods that you can read about on the internet (e.g. SleepEasy Solution, SuperNanny, etc). Use what you are comfy with.

NUTRITION:

o **Breast milk / formula should still be the ONLY form of nutrition.** Some parents choose to start solids (i.e. anything that is not milk) at this time and it **IS OKAY TO START ANYTIME BETWEEN 4-6 MONTHS with provider's support**, but speak to your provider **FIRST**. AAP recommends waiting until 6 months to start solids. See next chapter for feeding recommendations if you decide to start now.

o **Breast feed every 3-4 hours**. If you feel baby is still hungry after breastfeeding, breastfeed for longer or at more frequent intervals to increase supply OR you can supplement with formula AFTER each breastfeeding session

o **Bottle feed 5-7oz formula every 3-5 hours while awake**; do not force baby to finish.

o Have baby **practice holding the bottle** when feeding.

o **Continue to clean baby's gums and tongue** with a small washcloth first thing in the morning and after nighttime bottle.

GROWTH:

o **Height**: + 1 inch per month

o **Weight**: + 4-5 ounces per week (baby should be double birth weight now)

 Growth spurt is typical around **4 months**.

DEVELOPMENT:

Encourage tummy time throughout day – important for learning to roll over, crawl, and eventually walk. Baby should enjoy this a lot more now!

Keep feet exposed while baby plays (no socks) – this helps baby gauge movement better.

Baby is able to **regard own hand** and will start to bring hands together.

Baby will **reach with both hands**, bat at objects, grasp and hold onto toy (e.g. rattle).

Baby will **start to laugh and squeal.**

Will use a **raking grasp** (not use individual fingers yet).

Baby is able to **bring head up to 90°** when on tummy.

Baby is able to **start sitting with head steady** – have baby practice sitting by surrounding baby with pillows and using interesting toys to get baby to lean forward into sitting position. Can use Bumbo as well for few minutes at a time.

Baby will be **able to bear weight on legs** – stand baby up on your lap and watch the excitement.

Baby will **start to ROLL -** front to back first, then back to front.

HEALTH MAINTAINANCE:

Continue **2-3 baths** per week and moisturize afterwards.

Continue **diaper-free time** every day (10-20 minutes).

Adapt routine to baby's changing needs (may need to space out time set aside for naps).

PEDIATRIC VISITS:

o **Well child visit at 4 months** – VACCINE time. Shots: DTap, Hib, PCV, IPV. By mouth: Rotavirus (see Appendix A for explanations).

TID BITS:

o This is a good time to **go on vacation**! Go before baby is crawling and starts solids, now that you have the hang of it!

o This is a good time for **baby portraits**! Again, before baby is too mobile and won't sit still for them.

o **NEVER take your hands off baby** when on a high surface (like a changing table) – one day baby will surprise you and roll right off!

o Create **a safe area for baby** for when you need to step away (e.g. Pack n' Play).

o Baby is **continuing to make associations**, so think about your habits (constantly holding baby, rocking baby to sleep, etc.) and **continue decreasing / eliminating any "bad" habits now**.

o Continue to **READ** to baby! Pick simple word books now (colors, shapes, animals, etc.).

GOALS TO WORK TOWARDS:

o Think about **weaning the pacifier**.

o Get a **sippy/straw cup** – next month you will introduce that

o Baby **may start teething**, so figure out what you feel comfortable using for pain relief and get it ready. For pain you can use teething rings, cold washcloths from freezer, frozen baby teething toys, baby Orajel, clove oil and/or cold whole peeled carrots.

BABY-PROOF ENTIRE HOME – baby is about to take over the house (if he / she hasn't already)! If you are not sure what needs to be proofed, invite an 8-12 month over and you will learn quickly ☺ (e.g. **cabinet locks, stair gates, corners/edges, gas knob covers, outlet plugs, etc**.).

If baby is bottle feeding and is working hard to get the milk out, **think about going up a nipple size.**

MILESTONE: CRAWLING

METHOD: Place baby in the crawling position and sway baby's hips back and forth. Try this while baby plays. Once baby can figure out how to sync movements to move forward, baby will start to crawl. Expect baby to just move hands forward at first and fall on tummy. That's okay. Encourage baby to get back on all fours and try again. Crawling can be in many forms – traditional hands and knees, army style, using one leg and one arm style, oh they can get very creative!

NOTES:

Months 6 & 7 - Halfway there! Already!?!

SLEEP:

~15 hours a day with 2-3 naps/day – stretch of sleep at night will start to get longer (6-11 hours), but **night waking is still common** (4-6 times a night) – try not to pick baby up, let him or her self-soothe.

White noise still OKAY.

Enforce transitional object that is only associated with sleep – will help baby self-soothe when you are not there.

Put baby in crib for all naps and sleep when at home.

ROUTINE ROUTINE ROUTINE!

NUTRITION:

o **Breast milk/formula should still be the PRIMARY form of nutrition, but it's** <u>safe to start solids</u> **now! (see Appendix E)**

o **Aim to use same place (e.g. high chair) for feeding until baby has a good grasp, in an upright position, not somewhere where baby sleeps (e.g. bouncer).**

Start with cereals / veggies then introducing fruits later. Babies seem to like the sweetness of fruits and will hate peas after apples. ☺

o **One new food every 3-4 days.**

o **Start with 1 tablespoon per meal**, increasing slowly to 2 tablespoons per meals, with the **GOAL of** 3 tablespoons per meal.

- Sometimes babies **prefer food warm**, so keep a heating source close by (but a safe distance from baby).
- **Once you have tried a certain food**, you can start to mix in a new food for 3-4 days (e.g. once you have tried apples, you can try apples and sweet potatoes for 3-4 days; then you can try apples, sweet potatoes and peas for 3-4 days). Try to stick to 2-3 flavors max until baby gets good at eating.
- Use a **soft tip spoon** to protect baby's gums.
- Since **baby is very curious** about the world, you may need toys to entertain with during feedings. Use toys that are easy to clean (e.g. bath books – avoid gadgets like iPhones!!!).
- Keep a **wet washcloth handy** for when things get messy.
- **SIGNS OF ALLERGY** to food = RASH, hives, diarrhea, vomiting, difficulty breathing. **If baby has difficulty breathing, call 911 immediately**.
- **Provide teething relief,** if needed, 10-15 minutes before mealtime.
- Can start to give baby **1-2oz of water per day** from a sippy/straw cup.
- **Breastfeed every 3-4 hours.**
- **Bottle feed 6-8oz formula every 4-6 hours** while awake.
- **Have baby hold the bottle** while feeding – should be able to feed self.

- ○ **Clean baby's gums and tongue** with a small washcloth.
- ○ **If baby has teeth,** use a baby finger brush to clean teeth in morning and at bedtime after last bottle and after each meal if preferred. Use FLUORIDE FREE toothpaste only (e.g. Baby Orajel, Colgate, Earth's Best).
- ○ **DO NOT PUT BABY TO SLEEP WITH A BOTTLE IN MOUTH** – this will cause dental cavities! Make sure you are cleaning baby's mouth after last feeding.

GROWTH:

Height: + ½ inch per month
Weight: + 4-5 ounces per week

 Growth spurt is typical around **6 months.**

DEVELOPMENT

Keep feet exposed while baby plays (no socks).
Baby is able to **sit with minimal support** (goal is sitting by 7 months).
Baby is able to **roll in both directions** and may start to do continuous rolls.
Baby is able to **reach with one hand.**
Baby is able to **transfer objects** from one hand to the other.
Baby will bring **feet to mouth.**
Baby **BABBLES** – mamama, dadadada, babababa, nananana.
Baby will **start to show displeasure** when parents leave the room. Talk to baby when leaving and returning.
Baby will **imitate play**, so get creative: make funny faces,

funny noises and act silly. This is the best audience you will ever have!

HEALTH MAINTAINANCE:

o   Continue only **2-3 baths** per week and moisturize afterwards.

o   Continue **diaper-free time** every day (10-20 minutes).

o   **Adapt routine** to baby's changing needs (may need to space out time set aside for naps).

PEDIATRIC VISITS:

o   **Well child visit at 6 months** – VACCINE time. Shots: Hep B #3 (given anywhere btw 6-12 months), DTap, Hib, PCV, IPV. By mouth: Rotavirus (see Appendix A for explanations).

o   Ask child's healthcare provider if it is necessary to add **FLUORIDE** to baby's vitamins – it's usually added if there is no fluoride in your drinking water.

TID BITS:

o   **Safe to use sunscreen** once baby is 6+ months old. Use a kid friendly one (Coppertone Water Babies, Neutrogena, etc).

o   Make sure to **supervise play time near pets** – baby is more mobile and may start to pull, swat, or push pets.

o   Baby may start **teething** – use pain relief as desired. **TEETHING** should **not** cause high fevers, cough, runny nose, vomiting, diarrhea etc. If you notice any of these symptoms there may be something else going on. Talk to child's healthcare provider.

Continue to **READ** to baby! Pick books with texture, flip up pages, or moving parts.

GOALS TO WORK TOWARDS:

Think about **transitioning from 3 naps to 2 naps** (if you are already at 2 naps you are ahead of the game!).

As baby continues to increase amount of solids, think about cutting **back on milk a little bit** (1/2-1oz per feed) – granted baby is consuming at least ~24 oz/day – or amount recommended by child's healthcare provider.

If baby is bottle feeding and is working hard to get the milk out, think about **going up a nipple size**.

MILESTONE: CRUISING

> **METHOD**: Use an object (e.g. sofa, bench, ottoman) at baby's chest height. Stand at one end and have baby at other end. Show baby a favorite toy and encourage him or her to move towards you along the object.

Months 6 & 7

NOTES:

_____

_____

_____

_____

_____

_____

_____

_____

_____

_____

_____

_____

_____

Months 8 & 9 - Sit, Creep, Crawl, Scoot!

SLEEP:

~15 hours a day with 2 naps / day –stretch of sleep at night will start to get longer (9-12 hours).

White noise still OKAY.

Enforce transitional object.

Put **baby in crib** for all naps and sleep when at home.

Night waking is still common (4-6 times a night).

ROUTINE ROUTINE ROUTINE!

NUTRITION:

Breast milk / formula should still be the PRIMARY form of nutrition (20-24oz/day).

Continue to use same area for feeding, builds association.

Provide teething relief, if needed, 10-15 minutes before mealtime.

SPICE IT UP: start to introduce spices into baby's food.

Use **sippy/straw cup** with water (1-2 oz).

Meal goals: 3 meals, 1-2 snacks.

Baby can **start to feed self food– provide finger foods** (Gerber Puffs, small pieces of cheese, steamed soft fruits/veggies, etc).

Breast feed every 3-4 hours.

Bottle feed formula 5-8oz every 3-4 hours.

Continue to clean baby's gums and tongue with a small washcloth/ baby toothbrush – still NO fluoride in toothpaste.

- ○ **DO NOT PUT BABY TO SLEEP WITH A BOTTLE IN MOUTH –** this will cause dental cavities! Make sure you are cleaning baby's mouth after last feeding.

GROWTH:

- ○ **Height**: + ½ inch per month
- ○ **Weight**: +2-4 ounces per week

Growth spurt is typical around **9 months.**

DEVELOPMENT:

- ○ **Keep feet exposed** while baby plays (no socks).
- ○ Baby **sits without support, pulls to stand, crawls.**
- ○ **Pincer grasp** develops - holding something with thumb and finger.
- ○ Baby **imitates speech sounds** -will copy when you say mamamama, dadadada, nananana, babababa.
- ○ Baby **understands and responds to "NO."**
- ○ **Baby understands and responds to own name**.
- ○ Baby is **building object permanence** - if you show a toy and then put it under blanket, baby may realize it is gone and look for it.
- ○ **Stranger anxiety develops** – try to have baby meet and go to as many people as you can (family and friends of course!).

HEALTH MAINTAINANCE:

- ○ Continue only **2-3 baths** per week and moisturize

afterwards.

Continue to **diaper-free time** every day (10-20 minutes).

Adapt routine to baby's changing needs.

EDIATRIC VISITS:

Well child visit at 9 months – health check; may get Hep B #3 or may get this at 12 months).

Ask provider if they do **vision screening** – otherwise you can ook online to find a clinic that does infant vision screening nfantSee program).

D BITS:

Stranger anxiety starts to peak. Reassure baby that you are around and try to warm baby up to people / surroundings if you notice baby getting wound up.

Avoid high anxiety moments when child is sick, tired, hungry, or in a new environment.

Transitional object is very important now for baby to feel safe.

Continue to **READ** to baby! Pick books that baby can handle, hold, grab, bite, and turn the pages of (I like bath books since the pages are plastic and easy to open / turn/ clean).

OALS TO WORK TOWARDS:

Practice sippy/straw cup.

Practice standing, scooting, crawling, cruising - holding onto furniture and walking. Walking is around the corner.

Some babies skip crawling all together, and will go from

scooting to walking, that is okay. Let baby get mobile however he or she is comfortable.

- **Make sure house is baby proofed!!!! Especially stairs and any cupboards baby can get into that may store chemicals.**
- If baby is bottle feeding and is working hard to get the milk out, **think about going up a nipple size.**
- You may start to notice that **baby is unwilling to fall asleep immediately** after being put down. You may need to stay in the room a few extra minutes before leaving. Try not to pick baby up if nothing is wrong. You can try to just sit quietly in sight but not hovering over crib or you can try to pat baby on back before slowly leaving room.
- **MILESTONE: WALKING**

  > **METHOD**: Hold baby by the hands and arms with baby's arms at his / her chest level (you don't want to practice with their arms in the air, because that i not how we walk once we learn how). Make sure baby is not wearing socks. Do not force baby. If baby is not showing signs of walking (cruising, standing and bouncing), try again the following week.

NOTES:

_____

_____

_____

_____

GOALS towards the big 1 YEAR mark:

At 11 ¾ months, **start to transition from breast milk (BM) / formula (F) to whole cow's milk (WM).** At age one, baby will transition fully to **whole milk** unless a milk allergy is diagnosed.

> **METHOD**: Use ¾ BM/F + ¼ WM → ½ BM/F + ½ WM → ¼ BM/F + ¾ WM → all whole milk OR you can transition cold turkey, substituting one feed at a time. You can transition over the 2 weeks surrounding the first birthday or after baby turns 1.

If baby is bottle feeding and working hard to get the milk out, **think about going up a nipple size.** Focus on **transitioning baby to sippy/straw cup by ~15 months.** Think about baby's 1st birthday celebration and make sure to **schedule the 1 year well child visit for a few days after** so that baby can enjoy the celebration too!

> Your provider cannot give baby the one year vaccines even a day before baby's 1st birthday, so make the appt accordingly!

TAKE A DEEP BREATH: you are almost the parents of a ONE YEAR OLD TODDLER! Boy that went FAST!

SLEEP:

~13 hours a day with 2 naps/day – with longest stretch of sleep at night (9-12 hours).

- ○ **White noise** still OKAY.
- ○ **Enforce transitional object.**
- ○ Put **baby in crib** for all naps and sleep when at home.
- ○ **Night waking** is diminishing. Baby should be able to self-soothe.
- ○ **ROUTINE ROUTINE ROUTINE!**

NUTRITION:

- ○ **Breast milk/formula should still be the PRIMARY form of nutrition (16-24oz / day) until 12 months.**
- ○ **Breast feed every 4-5 hours**.
- ○ **Bottle feed 6-8oz formula every 4-6 hours.**
- ○ **At 12 MONTHS, baby will transition to WHOLE COW'S MILK – baby needs the calories so don't use low fat milk!**
- ○ **Baby can start to eat what the family is eating but more bland** (not too spicy / salty / sweet).
- ○ Provide teething relief, if needed, 10-15 minutes before mealtime. Need for teething relief should lessen by now.
- ○ **Continue to use sippy/straw cup** for water – can start to use milk for 1x / day if baby takes to it; otherwise stick to water for now. A good time to *try* transitioning is when switching to cow's milk.
- ○ **Meal goals**: 3 meals, 1-3 snacks.
- ○ **Baby can feed self** – provide finger foods and start introducing a child-safe spoon. Put a tablecloth under baby's eating area to make clean up easier.
- ○ **Continue to clean baby's gums and tongue** with a small washcloth / baby toothbrush - still NO fluoride in

toothpaste.
DO NOT PUT BABY TO SLEEP WITH A BOTTLE IN MOUTH – this will cause cavities! Make sure you are cleaning baby's mouth after last feeding.

ROWTH:

Height: + ½ inch per month
Weight: + 2-4 ounces per week (by 12 months, baby may have TRIPLED birth weight!)

Growth spurt is typical around **12 months** – may also coincide with teething, ☹ double whammy.

EVELOPMENT:

Keep feet exposed while baby plays and now learns to WALK – no socks.
Baby **is able to stand, cruise (walk holding furniture) and scoot.**
When **WALKING,** baby will start with arms out to side and feet shoulder-width apart and everything will come closer to the middle with experience! ☺
Baby **plays pat-a-cake and imitates** activities.
Baby **is able to wave** hi and bye.
Baby **recognizes objects and POINTS** – use words to describe what baby points to (e.g. that's the fan, that's the window, that's the light). Then ask baby to point to the objects (e.g. where is the fan, where is the light).
Baby begins to **use "dada" / "mama" specifically**.
Baby **stands for 2 seconds without support.**

- Baby may start to **play ball** (roll ball in your direction).
- Baby **imitates speech sounds**.
- Baby very much **understands cause-and-effect** – try to ignore tantrums, attend to real boo-boos and let baby problem solve (e.g. If baby is stuck under a toy, let him / her figure out how to get out instead of running to the rescue, assuming he / she is out of harm's way). Engage baby when happy / playful.
- Baby is starting to **understand language** – baby should know 5-10 words by 12 months. If you're cursing, now is the time to STOP!
- At 12 months, baby can **cooperate**, so practice commands with baby often.

HEALTH MAINTAINANCE:
- Continue only **2-3 baths** per week and moisturize afterwards.
- Continue **diaper-free time** every day (10-20 minutes).
- **Adapt your routine** to baby's changing needs.
- **Baby MAY transition to one nap** (may still need 2) – go with baby's cues.

PEDIATRIC VISITS:
- **Well child visit at 12 months** – SHOTS: Varicella #1, PCV, PPD along with blood work, lead check, urine check, hearing screen. Some pediatric offices may not do all the aforementioned tests – so ask child's healthcare provider if you are not sure (see Appendix A).

ID BITS:

This is a **time of great change** and with all these shifts, baby may become frustrated. Just remember to keep your cool. If you feel your child is giving you a hard time, it is likely that he or she is having a hard time. Be patient.

Try to **expose baby to as much as you can –** new activities, textures, environments, people, etc. It will help expand baby's knowledge of this amazing world.

Continue to **READ** to baby! Pick books with simple words that baby can recognize (up, down, in, out) as well as peek-a-boo books with colors and shapes.

Remember to enjoy these last few months; take pictures, go out for walks, sing songs, read books, spend time together as a family, and cuddle a lot! Before you know it baby will be one and onto toddlerhood. And even though there are so many GREAT things to come, nothing will trump all the amazing achievements your little bundle made through his/her first year of life!

NOTES:

APPENDICES

APPENDIX A

APPENDIX B

APPENDIX C

APPENDIX D

APPENDIX E

APPENDIX F

CDC Vaccine Chart

Information on vaccines obtained from www.cdc.gov

Vaccine ▼	Age ▶	Birth	1 mo	2 mo	4 mo	6 mo	9 mo	12 mo	15 mo	18 mo	19-23 mo	2-3 yrs	4-6 yrs
Hepatitis B	HepB	#1	#2	#2		#3	#3	#3	#3	#3			
Rotavirus	RV			#1	#2	#3							
Diphtheria, tetanus, pertussis	DTaP			#1	#2	#3			#4	#4			#5
Haemophilus influenza type b	Hib			#1	#2	#3		#4	#4				
Pneumococcal	PCV			#1	#2	#3		#4	#4				
Inactivated poliovirus	IPV			#1	#2	#3	#3	#3	#3	#3			#4
Influenza						1 shot yearly							
Measles, mumps, rubella	MMR							#1					#2
Varicella (chicken pox)								#1					#2
Hepatitis A	HepA							#1	#1	#1	#1	Hep A Series	Hep A Series

*Larger boxes indicate the age range when a vaccine can be given.

53

CDC Vaccine Explanations

>DIPHTHERIA - part of DTaP vaccine - *Bacteria*
You can get it from contact with an infected person. Signs and symptoms include a thic covering in the back of the throat that can make it hard to breathe. It can lead t breathing problems, heart failure and death.

>TETANUS (lockjaw) - part of DTaP vaccine – *Bacteria*
You can get it from a cut or wound. It does not spread from person to person. Signs an symptoms include painful tightening of the muscles, usually all over the body. It can lea to stiffness of the jaw, so the victim can't open his mouth or swallow. It leads to death i about 1 case out of 5.

>PERTUSSIS (whooping cough) – part of DTaP vaccine - *Bacteria*
You can get it from contact with an infected person. Signs and symptoms include violer coughing spells that can make it hard for an infant to eat, drink, or breathe. These spell can last for weeks. It can lead to pneumonia, seizures (jerking and staring spells), brai damage, and death.

>HAEMNOPHILUS INFLUENZAE TYPE B (HIB) - *Bacteria*
You can get it from contact with an infected person. Signs and symptoms. There may b no signs or symptoms in mild cases. It can lead to meningitis (infection the brain an spinal cord coverings); pneumonia; infections of the blood, joints, bones, and coverin of the heart; brain damage; deafness; and death.

>HEPATITIS B (HEP B*) - Virus*
You can get it from contact with blood or body fluids of an infected person. Babies ca get it at birth if the mother is infected, or through a cut or wound. Adults can get it fror unprotected sex, sharing needles or other exposures to blood. Signs and symptom include tiredness, diarrhea and vomiting, jaundice (yellow skin or eyes), and pain i muscles, joints and stomach. It can lead to liver damage, liver cancer, and death.

>POLIO (IPV) - *Virus*
You can get it from contact with an infected person. It enters the body through th mouth. Signs and symptoms can include a cold-like illness, or there may be no signs c symptoms at all. It can lead to paralysis or death (by paralyzing breathing muscles).

>PNEUMOCOCCAL (PCV) - *Bacteria*
You can get it from contact with an infected person. Signs and symptoms include feve chills, cough and chest pain. It can lead to meningitis (infection of the brain and spin cord coverings), blood infections, ear infections, pneumonia, deafness, brain damag and death.

ROTAVIRUS (RV) - *Virus*
You can get it from contact with other children who are infected. Signs and symptoms include severe diarrhea, vomiting and fever. It can lead to dehydration, hospitalization (up to about 70,000 kids are hospitalized per year) and death.

MEASLES – part of MMR vaccine - *Virus*
Can spread from person to person through the air. Causes rash, cough, runny nose, eye irritation and fever. Can lead to ear infection, pneumonia, seizures, brain damage and death.

MUMPS – part of MMR vaccine - *Virus*
Can spread from person to person through the air. Causes fever, headache and swollen glands. Can lead to deafness, meningitis (infection of the brain and spinal cord covering), infection of the pancreas, painful swelling of the testicles or ovaries, and, rarely, death.

RUBELLA (German Measles) – part of MMR vaccine - *Virus*
Can spread from person to person through the air. Causes rash and mild fever and can cause arthritis (mostly in women). If a woman gets rubella while she is pregnant, she could have a miscarriage or her baby could be born with serious birth defects.

VARICELLA (Chickenpox) - *Virus*
Can spread from person to person through the air and through contact with fluid from chickenpox blisters. Causes rash, itching, fever, tiredness. Can lead to severe skin infection, scars, pneumonia, brain damage or death.

HEPATITIS A (Hep A) - *Virus*
Spread by close personal contact and sometimes by eating food or drinking water containing HAV. A person who has hepatitis A can easily it to others within the same household. Can cause: "flu-like" illness, jaundice, severe stomach pains and diarrhea (children).

Tuberculosis (TB) (tested with PPD) - *Bacteria*
Caused by germs that are spread from person to person through the air. TB usually affects the lungs, but it can also affect other parts of the body, such as the brain, the kidneys, or the spine. Symptoms of TB include feelings of sickness or weakness, weight loss, fever, and night sweats.

MY BABY'S VACCINES:

*Insert dates/ages when vaccines were given.

Vaccine ▼	Age ▶	Birth	1 mo	2 mo	4 mo	6 mo	9 mo	12 mo	15 mo	18 mo	19-23 mo	2-3 yrs	4-6 yr
Hepatitis B	HepB												
Rotavirus	RV			5/29									
Diptheria, tetanus, pertussis	DTaP												
Haemophilus influenza type b	Hib												
Pneumococcal	PCV			5/29									
Inactivated poliovirus	IPV												
Influenza													
Measles, mumps, rubella	MMR												
Varicella (chicken pox)													
Hepatitis A	HepA												

FEEDING/DIAPERING LOG:

Indicates the side you started feeding on; next time start on opposite side.
BM= bottled breast milk

Time	Feeding			Diapering	
am/pm	Right breast (minutes)	Left Breast (minutes)	Formula/ BM (mLs)	Wet	Dirty
7a	15*	15		✓	✓

BREAST MILK STORAGE GUIDELINES:

*Chart obtained from:
http://www.cdc.gov/breastfeeding/recommendations/handling_breastmilk.htm

Location	Temp	Time	Comments
Countertop, table	Room temperature (up to 77°F or 25°C)	6–8 hours	Containers should be covered and kept as cool as possible; covering the container with a cold towel may keep milk cooler.
Insulated cooler bag	5–39°F or -15–4°C	24 hours	Keep ice packs in contact with milk containers at all times; limit opening cooler bag.
Refrigerator	39°F or 4°C	5 days	Store milk in the back of the main body of the refrigerator.
Freezer			
Freezer compartment of a refrigerator	5°F or -15°C	2 weeks	Store milk toward the back of the freezer, where temperature is most constant. Milk stored for longer durations in the ranges listed is safe, but some of the lipids in the milk undergo degradation resulting in lower quality.
Freezer compartment of refrigerator with separate doors	0°F or -18°C	3–6 months	
Chest or upright deep freezer	-4°F or -20°C	6–12 months	

Reference: Academy of Breastfeeding Medicine. (2004) Clinical Protocol Number #8: Human Milk Storage Information for Home Use for Healthy Full Term Infants. Princeton Junction, New Jersey: Academy of Breastfeeding Medicine.

SLEEP / FEED SCHEDULES:

Schedules are SO important because they let baby know what to expect. Schedules create predictability. This way you can plan your day better too! So, whatever times and order you choose, try to be consistent!

IN GENERAL:

Newborn – Feeding / naps / play are on baby's time. At 7a, move baby to family area, even for naps. At 7p, move baby to quiet area for nighttime sleep.

1-2 months – The first few months you will basically be trying to get baby on a schedule, so do not fret if you are not getting it exactly as described – just go with the flow and use the below as guidelines. Your baby may need to eat more frequently, sleep through feed times and may not want to play. Things will get better... have faith.

4-5 months –Baby should have a pretty good schedule now.

7-8 months – Baby may start to transition to two naps.

10-11-12 months – Baby *may* start to transition to one nap by 12 months.

Feel free to adjust the following schedules to fit your baby and family's lifestyle. These are just <u>examples</u> to get you started!

0-1-2 months:

7a	**CHANGE** - bring to family room / normal noise level (naps can happen between 7a and 7p, however baby prefers) **FEED** – breast milk or formula **PLAY** – age appropriate activity
8a-10a	NAP
10a	**CHANGE** **FEED** – breast milk or formula **PLAY** – bath (sponge / tub – every 2-3 days)
11a-1p	NAP
1p	**CHANGE** **FEED** – breast milk or formula **PLAY**
2p-4p	NAP
4p	**CHANGE** **FEED** – breast milk or formula **PLAY**
5-6p	NAP
7p	**CHANGE** **FEED** – breast milk or formula **BACK TO SLEEP** – move to quiet time until morning
10p	**CHANGE** – quiet, dim, no interaction **FEED** – breast milk or formula (try to cut this feed out by 2-3 months) **BACK TO SLEEP**
1a	**CHANGE** – quiet, dim, no interaction **FEED** – breast milk or formula **BACK TO SLEEP**
4a	**CHANGE** – quiet, dim, no interaction **FEED** – breast milk or formula (try to cut this feed out by 3-4 months) **BACK TO SLEEP**

* If baby wakes in the middle of a scheduled feed during nighttime, try to console baby with rocking first. If baby persists, you may need to feed.

APPENDIX D

3-4-5 months:

OPTION 1

7a	**CHANGE** – bring to family room, normal noise level **FEED** – breast milk or formula **PLAY**
9a-11a	NAP
11a	**CHANGE** **FEED** – breast milk or formula **PLAY**
1p-3p	NAP
3p	**CHANGE** **FEED** – breast milk or formula **PLAY**
4p-4:45p	POWER NAP
7p	**CHANGE** – move to dim place for night, quiet time until morning **FEED** – breast milk or formula ***wipe mouth after feed **BACK TO SLEEP**
1a	**CHANGE** - quiet, dim, no interaction **FEED** – try to cut this feed out by 4-5 months **BACK TO SLEEP**

* Can add bath at 12:30p or 5:30p

* If you decide to start solids before 6 months, see next schedule for month 6-7-8.

This is for when baby is sleeping through the night.

7a-9a	**CHANGE** **FEED** – breast milk or formula **BACK TO SLEEP (NAP)**
9a	**CHANGE** – bring to family room, normal noise level **FEED** – breast milk or formula **PLAY**
11a-1p	**NAP**
1p	**CHANGE** **FEED** – breast milk or formula **PLAY**
3p-3:45p	**POWER NAP**
4p	**CHANGE** **FEED** – breast milk or formula **PLAY**
7p	**CHANGE** – move to dim place for night, quiet time until morning **FEED** – breast milk or formula ***wipe mouth after feed **BACK TO SLEEP**

Can add bath at 10:30a or 5:30p

APPENDIX D

MY BABY'S SCHEDULE AT 3-5 months

7-8 months:
May start to transition to 2 naps

OPTION 1

7a	**CHANGE** – bring to family room, normal noise level **FEED** – BREAKFAST + breast milk or formula **PLAY**
9a-11a	**NAP**
11a	**CHANGE** **FEED** – LUNCH + breast milk or formula **PLAY**
1p-3p	**NAP**
3p	**CHANGE** **FEED** – SNACK = breast milk or formula **PLAY**
4p-4:45p	**POWER NAP** - phase this nap out between 6-8 months
6p	**FEED** – DINNER
7p	**CHANGE** – move to dim / quiet place until morning **FEED** – breast milk or formula ***wipe mouth after feed **BACK TO SLEEP**

Can add bath at 12:30p or 6:30p – before last bottle

7a-9a	**CHANGE** **FEED** – breast milk or formula **BACK TO SLEEP** (**NAP**)
9a	**CHANGE** – bring to family room, normal noise level **FEED** – BREAKFAST + breast milk or formula **PLAY**
11a-12p	**NAP**
12p	**CHANGE** **FEED** – LUNCH + breast milk or formula **PLAY**
3p	**CHANGE** **FEED** – SNACK = breast milk or formula **PLAY**
3p-4:30p	**NAP**
6pm	**FEED** – DINNER
7pm	**CHANGE** – move to dim / quiet place until morning **FEED** – breast milk or formula ***wipe mouth after feed **BACK TO SLEEP**

MY BABY'S SCHEDULE AT 6-8 months

9-10-11-12 months
* Can do 8a-12p-4p-8p for meal times

7a	**CHANGE** – bring to family room, normal noise level **FEED** – BREAKFAST + breast milk or formula **PLAY**
9a-11a	**NAP**
11a	**CHANGE** **FEED** – LUNCH + breast milk or formula **PLAY**
1p-3p	**NAP**
3p	**CHANGE** **FEED** – SNACK + breast milk or formula **PLAY**
6p	**FEED** – DINNER
7p	**CHANGE** – move to dim place for night, quiet time until morning **FEED** – breast milk or formula ***wipe mouth after feed **BACK TO SLEEP**

EXAMPLE OF 1 NAP SCHEDULE:

7a	**CHANGE** – bring to family room, normal noise level **FEED** – BREAKFAST + breast milk or formula **PLAY**
11a	**CHANGE** **FEED** – LUNCH + breast milk or formula **PLAY**
12p-3p	**NAP**
3p	**CHANGE** **FEED** – SNACK + breast milk or formula **PLAY**
6p	**FEED** – DINNER
7p	**CHANGE** – move to dim place for night, quiet time until morning **FEED** – breast milk or formula ***wipe mouth after feed **BACK TO SLEEP**

MY BABY'S SCHEDULE AT 9-10 months

MY BABY'S SCHEDULE AT 11-12 months

STARTING SOLIDS:

○ **ALWAYS GIVE SOLIDS WITH A SPOON** and not in a bottle – including rice cereal - until introducing finger foods, that is!

○ **Start off slow and steady.** Introduce one new thing every 3-5 days. LUNCH is a good time to try new stuff!

○ Start with **the BASIC FIRST FOODS** list (see pg. 75). Once ALL those foods have been tried, you can start introducing new foods mixed with the basic first foods (e.g. sweet potato and carrot with carrot as new food).

○ When you use milk in cereal / food, it **counts as milk for that meal** (2oz milk + 3 tbsp cereal + 4oz bottle means baby had 6oz milk that meal).

WHEN STORING FOOD IN FRIDGE OR FREEZER:
> **FRIDGE** (≤ 40° F): 1-2 days
> **FREEZER** (0° F): 2-3 months; however, once thawed use within 24 hours

MEASUREMENTS:
1 teaspoon (tsp) = 5mL
1 tablespoon (tbsp) = 15 mL = ½ ounce (oz)
2 tablespoons (tbsp) = 30 mL = 1 ounce (oz)
4 tablespoons (tbsp) = 60 mL = ¼ cup

ounces = volume of food   grams = weight of food

HIGHLY ALLERGIC FOODS:
Wait until ONE YEAR of age to introduce,
or as directed by your child's healthcare provider.
-Cow's Milk   -Eggs   -Soy   -Shellfish
-Peanuts   -Fish   -Wheat   -Tree nuts (e.g. walnut)

SERVINGS FOR AGE GROUPS PER DAY:

Below are approximate recommendations. Baby may be able to eat this much or may not. Go with baby's cues.

6-8 months:
2-4oz grains
4-8oz fruits / veggies

8-10 months:
4-6oz grains
4oz protein
8-10oz fruits / veggies

10+ months:
6-8oz grains
4-6oz protein
2oz dairy
8-10oz fruits / veggies

NEVER re-refrigerate or re-freeze food left over from the bowl your baby has been eating from. Once the spoon has been in your baby's mouth and back into the bowl, the food has been contaminated with your baby's saliva which contains bacteria that can grow in the food. So, food must be eaten within the hour or thrown out.

For table purposes:
Milk = breast milk or formula

BREASTMILK / FORMULA AMOUNTS HAVE NOT BEEN INCLUDED ON THESE TABLES. THESE ARE SIMPLY FOR SOLIDS.

MEAL PLANS

First week of solids:

* Food will start off watery and get more textured as baby gets used to eating solids. As amount of food increases, either keep the amount of milk constant or, if very runny, decrease milk by small amounts.

	LUNCH
MON	1 tsp rice cereal + 1 oz milk
TUES	1 tbsp rice cereal + 1-2oz milk
WED	1-2 tbsp rice cereal + 1-2oz milk
THURS	2 tbsp rice cereal + 1-2oz milk
FRI	1 tsp oatmeal + 1-1.5 tbsp rice cereal + 1oz milk
SAT	1 tbsp oatmeal + 1 tbsp rice cereal + 1oz milk
SUN	1-2 tbsp oatmeal + 1-2oz milk

*** 2 tbsp max is what you will offer. Baby may not finish it all.

Second week of solids:

* If baby is finishing meals, you can up the amount until you get to about 2oz of food per meal.

	LUNCH
MON	2 tbsp oatmeal + 1-1½ oz milk
TUES	1tsp barley + 1-1.5 tbsp oatmeal + 1oz milk
WED	1 tbsp barley + 1 tbsp oatmeal + 1oz milk
THURS	1-2 tbsp barley + 1-2oz milk
FRI	2 tbsp barley + 1-1½ oz milk
SAT	1 tsp sweet potato + 1-1½ tbsp any cereal + 1-2oz milk, if needed
SUN	2 tsp sweet potato + ½ -1½ tbsp any cereal + 1-2oz milk, if needed

Third week of solids:

Take your time. Baby may need more than 2-3 weeks to start 2 meals a day. Once baby is finishing all the food, try increasing to 2 meals.

	LUNCH	DINNER
MON	1 tbsp sweet potato + ½ -1 tbsp any cereal + 1-2oz milk, if needed	2-4 tbsp any cereal + 1-3oz milk
TUES	1-2 tbsp sweet potato + ½ -1 tbsp any cereal if needed + 1-2oz milk, if needed	2-4 tbsp any cereal + 1-3oz milk
WED	1 tsp squash + 1-1½ tbsp any cereal OR sweet potato + 1-2oz milk, if needed	2-4 tbsp any cereal + 1-3oz milk
THURS	2 tsp squash + ½ -1½ tbsp any cereal + 1-2oz milk, if needed	2-4 tbsp sweet potato + milk as needed
FRI	1 tbsp squash + ½ -1 tbsp any cereal OR sweet potato + 1-2oz milk, if needed	2-4 tbsp any cereal + 1-3oz milk
SAT	1-2 tbsp squash + ½ -1 tbsp any cereal if needed + 1-2oz milk, if needed	2-4 tbsp sweet potato + milk as needed
SUN	1 tsp apple + 1-1½ tbsp any cereal OR sweet potato OR squash + 1-2oz milk, if needed	2-4 tbsp any cereal + 1-3oz milk

APPENDIX E

THREE <u>MEALS</u> A DAY:

6+ months

	BREAKFAST	LUNCH	SNACK	DINNER
MON	Cereal + yogurt	Fruit	Milk	Veggies
TUES	Cereal + fruit	Yogurt + Fruit	Milk	Veggies
WED	Cereal + yogurt	Fruit	Milk	Veggies
THURS	Cereal + fruit	Yogurt + Fruit	Milk	Veggies
FRI	Cereal + yogurt	Fruit	Milk	Veggies
SAT	Cereal + fruit	Yogurt + Fruit	Milk	Veggies
SUN	Cereal + yogurt	Fruit	Milk	Veggies

* You can also split meals so that baby gets veggies and fruit for lunch and dinner. You can also swap when baby gets fruits and veggies (see below). You can add carbs/cereal to any meal too. Take liberty in your preferences! ☺

8+ months

	BREAKFAST	LUNCH	SNACK	DINNER
MON	Cereal + yogurt	Veggies + protein + cheese	Milk + snack	Fruit + Veggie + Carb
TUES	Cereal + fruit	Yogurt + Fruit	Milk + snack	Veggies + protein + cheese
WED	Cereal + yogurt	Veggies + protein + cheese	Milk + snack	Fruit + Veggie + Carb
THURS	Cereal + fruit	Yogurt + Fruit	Milk + snack	Veggies + protein + cheese
FRI	Cereal + yogurt	Veggies + protein + cheese	Milk + snack	Fruit + Veggie + Carb
SAT	Cereal + fruit	Yogurt + Fruit	Milk + snack	Veggies + protein + cheese
SUN	Cereal + yogurt	Veggies + protein + cheese	Milk + snack	Fruit + Veggie + Carb

* You can give meals as above or you can split meals or food groups as desired. Take liberty in your preferences!

* You can wait to introduce a snack with milk until one year of age (during 3rd feeding). Snacks can be anything (fruit, yogurt, puffs, etc.).

APPENDIX E

74

FOODS LIST:

When unsure check with baby's provider to make sure all foods listed are acceptable to their practice for your child.

+ months:
BASIC FIRST FOODS/ Stage 1:
GRAINS: rice, oat, barley
FRUITS: apple, pear, banana
VEGGIES: avocado, squash (acorn/butternut), zucchini (same as green squash), sweet potato (same as yams), green bean

+ months: start adding finger foods
Stage 2
GRAINS: mixed grain cereal, millet, flax, buckwheat, bread, pastina, Gerber puffs
FRUITS: peach, apricot, cantaloupe, plum, watermelon, pineapple, mango, papaya, prune, berries (careful to cut to small pieces), kiwi
VEGGIES: pea, asparagus, carrot, white potato, broccoli, cauliflower, turnip, kale, eggplant, spinach
PROTEIN: beans (chickpea/kidney/lima/black eyed), lentils, chicken, turkey, tofu
DAIRY: yogurt (whole milk), cottage cheese, cream cheese, cheeses (no soft cheese (e.g. Brie) until one year old) – can start with Cheddar/Colby-Jack/American

10+ months:
Stage 3
GRAINS: pasta, bread, bagels, wheat cereals (i.e. Cheerios)
FRUITS: citrus fruits, cherries, dates, grapes
VEGGIES: corn, beets, brussel sprouts, cucumbers, tomatoes
PROTEIN: eggs (yolk only until 12 months), fish
DAIRY: whole milk after 12 months, stronger cheeses

APPENDIX E

BASIC INFANT ANATOMY:

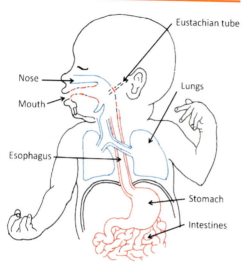

Eustachian tube

Nose

Mouth

Lungs

Esophagus

Stomach

Intestines

■ **Respiratory Tract**   ■ **Gastrointestinal Tract**
(DASHED LINES INDICATE OVERLAP OF THE TWO SYSTEMS)

* This diagram shows the respiratory (breathing) tract and the gastrointestinal (eating) tract.

VOMITING: Food/milk goes through the mouth, down the esophagus, and into the stomach where it is digested. When a baby vomits, it means the stomach muscle is forcefully pushing the food the opposite way: **UP** the esophagus and out of the mouth. Since the back of the throat and the back of the nose are connected, sometimes food may come out of the nose when vomiting, and that is okay. Once baby is settled, gently clean the nose, nostrils and mouth with a wet wash cloth, being careful not to go too far back.

EUSTACHIAN TUBE: This is a small tube that connects the inside of the ear with the back of the throat. When your ears "pop" you are basically releasing pressure that has built up in the back of the ear through the canal. When you feed baby in a 'flat-on-back' position, you risk milk potentially traveling up the tube and causing an ear infection.

CHOKING: When a baby is choking, there is a blockage somewhere along the respiratory tract, starting from the back of the mouth down to the opening to the lungs. If this occurs, baby will not be able breathe from his / her mouth OR nose. CPR may be required. If baby sticks something up his / her nose, however, baby will still be able to breathe from the mouth. Seek help as needed.

ASTHMA: Inside the lungs, there are many more tiny tubes that take air into and out of the lungs. When a baby has asthma, some or all of the tubes in the respiratory tract, starting from the neck all the way through the ends inside the lungs, become inflamed and it becomes hard for baby to get air in and out of the air passage ways. When this happens, baby needs to get treatment (usually a nebulizer or inhaler) to help these passages relax so that air can get in and out of the lungs more easily. It is simply a matter of how quickly these passages become inflamed, and to what severity, that determines how fast treatment is needed. If you are concerned about your baby having asthma, please speak to your child's healthcare provider.

APPENDIX F

References:

Burn management: Burns. (2012). Retrieved February 1, 2012 from
http://kidshealth.org/parent/firstaid_safe/sheets/burns_sheet.html

Developmental Milestones: Frankenburg WK, Dodds JB. (1967). The Denver
developmental screening test. Journal of Pediatrics. Aug;71(2):181-91.

Immunizations: FIGURE 1: Recommended immunization schedule for persons
aged 0 through 6 years. (2011). Retrieved February 1, 2012 from
http://www.cdc.gov/vaccines/recs/schedules/downloads/child/0-6yrs-
schedule-pr.pdf

Immunization explanations: Vaccines and Preventable Diseases. (2009).
Retrieved February 1, 2012 from http://www.cdc.gov/vaccines/vpd-
vac/default.htm

Sleep parameters: Dixon & Stein - Encounters with Children: Pediatric
Behavior and Development (2005).

Weight and height growth: Dixon & Stein - Encounters with Children: Pediatric
Behavior and Development (2005).

Well child checks: Well Child Visits. (2012). Retrieved February 1, 2012 from
http://www.nlm.nih.gov/medlineplus/ency/article/001928.htm